Kindergarten - 2

Maths

Practice Book

AF644740

Copyright © Prints Publications Pvt Ltd

All rights reserved. This book is sold subject to the condition that it shall not, by way of trade or otherwise, be lent, resold, hired out, or otherwise circulated without the publisher's prior written consent, in any form of binding or cover or medium other than that in which it is published. No part of this book may be reproduced, stored in a retrieval system, or transmitted in any form or by any means, electronic mechanical, recording, photocopying, or otherwise, without the prior written permission from the copyright holder and the publisher.

Jurisdiction: Any conflict or dispute in relation to this publication shall be adjudged in accordance with the laws of India and the matter shall be subject to the jurisdiction of the Court, Tribunals or any other Forums of New Delhi, India only.

Published by

Prints Publications Pvt Ltd

Viraj Tower-2, 4259/3, Ansari Road,
Darya Ganj, New Delhi-110002
Tel. : +91-11-45355555
Fax: +91-11-23275542
E-mail : contact@printspublications.com
Website : www.printspublications.com

Concept by **Laveena Gupta**
Prepared by **Editorial and Research Team of Prints Publications Pvt Ltd**

ISBN: 9789393674968

Published and Printed by Mr. Pranav Gupta (Director) on behalf of Prints Publications Pvt Ltd, New Delhi, at Quarterfold Printabilities, India.

Preface

In our daily lives, numbers play an important role. As a result, it is essential to begin teaching youngsters how to write numerals at a young age. The Maths Practice Book for Kids will help your child understand numbers in both numerical and alphabetical order. This Book will assist them in improving their math skills and increasing their confidence. Through fun activities, the 'Kindergarten Maths Practice Book' will sharpen tiny learners' number skills.

This book is highly recommended for the students of CBSE & ICSE Board students, International Baccalaureate (IB) and Cambridge Curriculum. This series focuses on the overall development of the child.

CONTENTS

FORWARD COUNTING (1-19)

	T	O		T	O		T	O		T	O	
		1										

Date - ____________

Teacher's Signature - ____________

FORWARD COUNTING (1-19)

	T	O		T	O		T	O		T	O	
		1										

Date - ___________

Teacher's Signature - ___________

WHAT COMES AFTER (0-19)

	T	O		T	O		T	O		T	O	
		2						6				
		4						3				
		7						9				
		0					1	2				
		1					1	3				
		5					1	0				
		8					1	1				

Date - ____________

Teacher's Signature - ____________

WHAT COMES AFTER (1-19)

	T	O		T	O		T	O		T	O	
	1	2					1	3				
	1	4						9				
	1	7					1	2				
	1	0						6				
	1	1						3				
	1	5						8				
	1	8						5				

Date - ___________

Teacher's Signature - ___________

FILL IN THE MISSING NUMBERS (11-19)

Date - ____________

Teacher's Signature - ____________

COLOR EACH SHAPE AND DRAW AN OBJECT OF THE SAME SHAPE

Square

Rectangle

COLOR EACH SHAPE AND DRAW AN OBJECT OF THE SAME SHAPE

Circle

Triangle

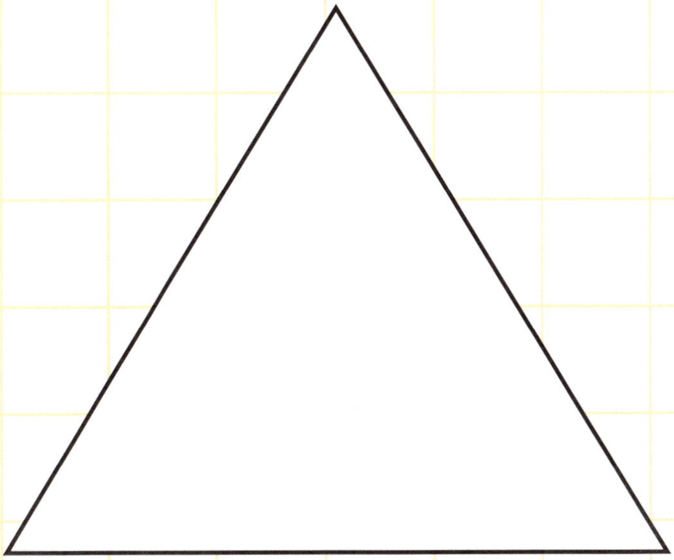

FORWARD COUNTING (20-29)

	T	O		T	O		T	O		T	O	
	2	0										

Date - ___________

Teacher's Signature - ___________

FORWARD COUNTING (1-29)

	T	O		T	O		T	O		T	O	
		1										

Date - ____________

Teacher's Signature - ____________

WHAT COMES AFTER (15-29)

T	O		T	O		T	O		T	O	
2	4					2	3				
2	6					2	2				
2	8					1	6				
2	5					1	8				
2	7					1	7				
2	1					1	9				
2	3					1	5				

Date - ____________

Teacher's Signature - ____________

MISSING NUMBERS (1-29)

T	O
1	5
___	___
___	___
1	8
___	___
___	___

T	O
2	3
___	___
2	5
___	___
___	___

WHAT COMES IN BETWEEN (1-29)

	T	O		T	O		T	O				
	1	2					1	4				
		9					1	1				
	2	5					2	7				
	1	7					1	9				
		3						5				
	1	0					1	2				
	1	9					2	1				

Date - ___________

Teacher's Signature - ___________

FORWARD COUNTING (30-39)

	T	O		T	O		T	O		T	O	
	3	0										

Date - ____________ Teacher's Signature - ____________

FORWARD COUNTING (1-39)

	T	O		T	O		T	O		T	O	
		1										

Date - ____________

Teacher's Signature - ____________

WHAT COMES AFTER (25-39)

	T	O		T	O		T	O		T	O	
	3	3					2	9				
	3	7					3	1				
	3	2					2	6				
	3	8					3	0				
	3	5					2	5				
	3	4					2	8				
	3	6					2	7				

Date - ___________

Teacher's Signature - ___________

WHAT COMES AFTER (1-39)

	T	O		T	O		T	O		T	O	
	2	5						5				
	1	9					1	1				
	3	8					1	4				
	1	7					2	9				
		4					2	6				
	2	2					3	6				
	3	0					2	0				

MISSING NUMBERS (1-39)

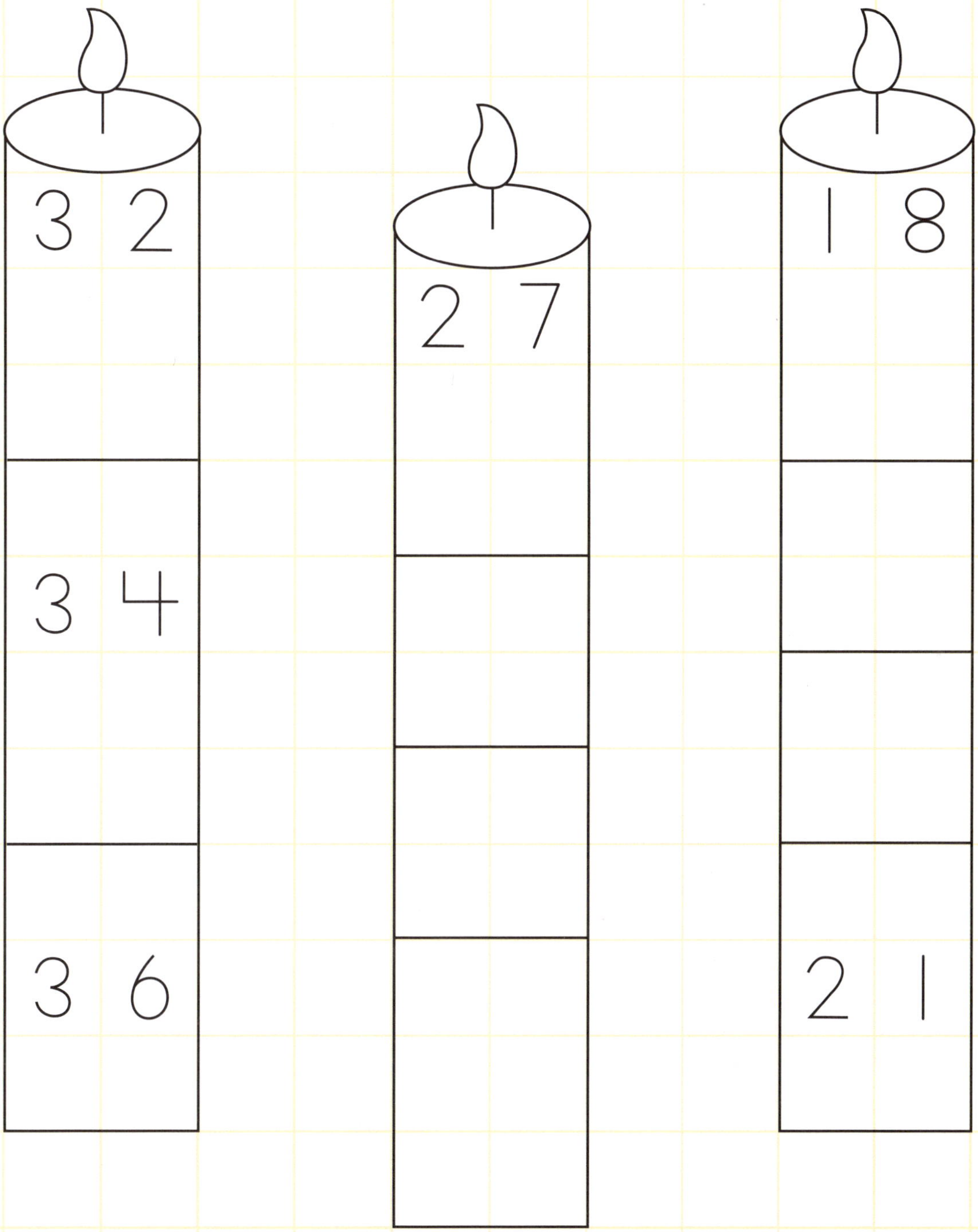

Date - ____________ Teacher's Signature - ____________

WHAT COMES IN BETWEEN (1-39)

T	O	T	O	T	O
3	0			3	2
2	7			2	9
1	9			2	1
1	1			1	3
3	5			3	7
3	7			3	9
2	0			2	2

Date - ____________

Teacher's Signature - ____________

COLOR THE SHAPE AND DRAW TWO OBJECTS OF THE SAME SHAPE

Oval

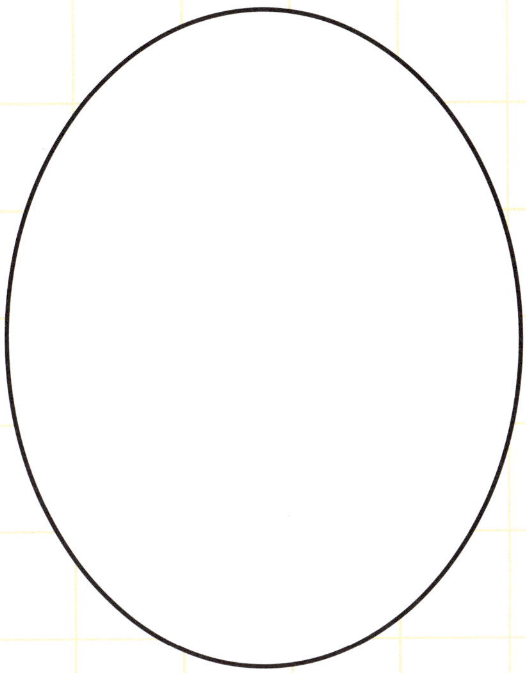

Date - ____________

Teacher's Signature - ____________

BACKWARD COUNTING (19-1)

	T	O		T	O		T	O		T	O	
	1	9										

Date - ____________

Teacher's Signature - ____________

BACKWARD COUNTING (39-21)

	T	O		T	O		T	O		T	O	
	3	9										

Date - ____________

Teacher's Signature - ____________

WHAT COMES BEFORE (1-19)

	T	O		T	O		T	O		T	O	
					2						3	
					5					1	0	
					9					1	7	
					1					1	5	
					8					1	9	
					4					1	1	
					7					1	6	

Date - __________

Teacher's Signature - __________

FORWARD COUNTING (40-49)

	T	O		T	O		T	O		T	O	
	4	0										

Date - ____________

Teacher's Signature - ____________

FORWARD COUNTING (1-49)

	T	O		T	O		T	O		T	O	
		1										

Date - ____________

Teacher's Signature - ____________

FORWARD COUNTING (40-49)

	T	O		T	O		T	O		T	O	
	4	0										

FORWARD COUNTING (1-49)

	T	O		T	O		T	O		T	O	
		1										

Date - ____________

Teacher's Signature - ____________

MISSING NUMBERS (30-49)

31			34	
	36	37		39
	41		43	
		47		

Date - ____________

Teacher's Signature - ____________

WHAT COMES IN BETWEEN (1-49)

T	O	T	O	T	O
2	3			2	5
4	7			4	9
3	4			3	6
1	8			2	0
3	9			4	1
4	4			4	6
2	2			2	4

BACKWARD COUNTING (19-10)

	T	O		T	O		T	O		T	O	
	1	9										

Date - ___________

Teacher's Signature - ___________

COLOR THE SHAPE AND DRAW TWO OBJECTS OF THE SAME SHAPE

Semi Circle

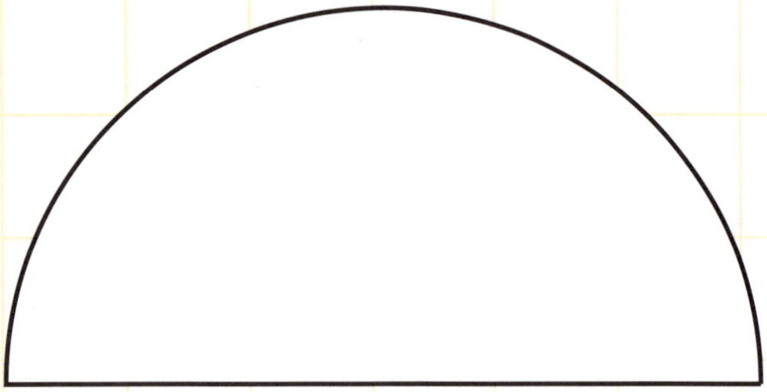

BACKWARD COUNTING (49-1)

	T	O		T	O		T	O		T	O	
	4	9										

Date - ____________

Teacher's Signature - ____________

WHAT COMES BEFORE (21-39)

T	O	T	O	T	O	T	O
		2	5			3	8
		3	5			2	2
		2	1			3	1
		2	4			2	6
		3	0			3	6
		2	8			3	2
		3	3			2	9

WHAT COMES BEFORE (31-49)

T	O	T	O	T	O	T	O
		4	7			3	8
		3	5			3	2
		3	1			4	1
		4	4			4	6
		4	0			3	6
		4	8			4	2
		3	3			3	9

Date - ___________

Teacher's Signature - ___________

CONNECT THE NUMBERS FROM (1-49)

FORWARD COUNTING (50-59)

	T	O		T	O		T	O		T	O	
	5	0										

Date - ___________

Teacher's Signature - ___________

FORWARD COUNTING (1-59)

	T	O		T	O		T	O		T	O	
		1										

FORWARD COUNTING (1-59)

	T	O		T	O		T	O		T	O	

Date - ____________

Teacher's Signature - ____________

MISSING NUMBERS (28-59)

T	O	T	O	T	O	T	O
2	8					5	2
2	9	3	7	4	5		
				4	6	5	4
		3	9				
3	2			4	8	5	6
3	3			4	9		
		4	2				
		4	3	5	1	5	9

Date - ____________ Teacher's Signature - ____________

BEFORE AND AFTER (50-59)

BEFORE		AFTER
	53	
	58	
	51	
	55	
	52	
	56	
	59	
	54	

BEFORE		AFTER
	50	
	52	
	56	
	53	
	57	
	51	
	54	
	55	

Date - ____________

Teacher's Signature - ____________

COLOR THE SHAPE AND DRAW TWO OBJECTS OF THE SAME SHAPE

Cylinder

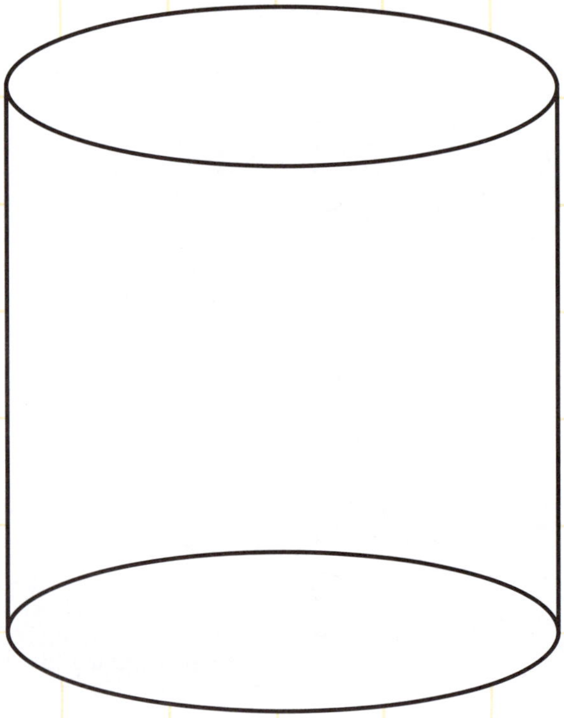

COUNT AND MATCH

9

6

10

8

11

Date - ____________

Teacher's Signature - ____________

BACKWARD COUNTING START FROM 49 AND GO TO 31

	T	O		T	O		T	O		T	O	
	4	9										
										3	1	

SHAPES

MATCH THE OBJECTS OF THE SAME SHAPE

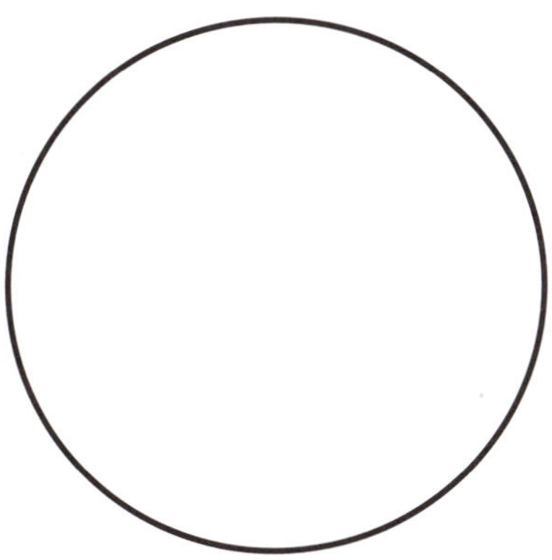

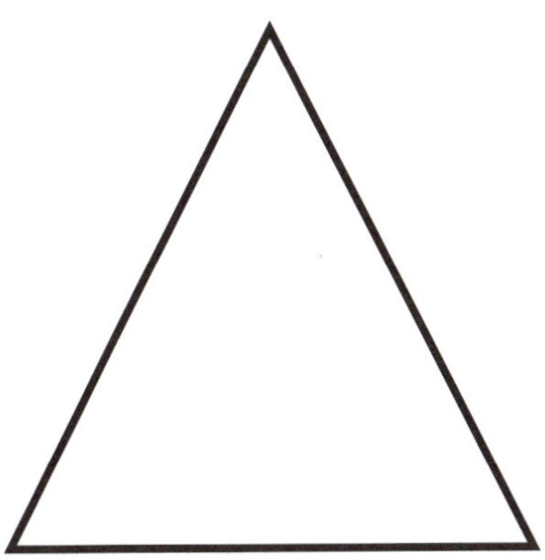

Date - ____________

Teacher's Signature - ____________

GREATER THAN / LESS THAN (< , >) (1-9)

is greater than >

< is less than

T	O		T	O
	7	☐		5
	0	☐		2
	9	☐		8
	4	☐		1
	3	☐		6
	5	☐		9
	6	☐		3

BIGGEST NUMBER (1-39)

Circle the biggest number in each row and write the number in the blank box.

T	O	T	O	T	O	T	O
1	2		7	2	5		
2	0	2	3	1	1		
1	2	3	1	3	2		
2	1	1	5	1	0		
2	2	1	8	2	9		
3	7	2	6	1	4		
2	9	3	9		9		

Date - ____________

Teacher's Signature - ____________

SMALLEST NUMBER (1-39)

Circle the smallest number in each row and write the number in the blank box.

T	O	T	O	T	O	T	O
	2	2	5	1	5		
2	7		1	3	6		
2	2		0	3	4		
3	9	3	2	3	0		
1	8	3	4	2	8		
1	4	2	2	3	0		
2	8	1	5		5		

Date - ____________

Teacher's Signature - ____________

FORWARD COUNTING (60-69)

	T	O		T	O		T	O		T	O	
	6	0										

FORWARD COUNTING (6-69)

T	O	T	O	T	O	T	O
	6	1	4			3	0
	7	1	5			3	1
				2	4		
						3	3
1	0					3	4
1	1	1	9				
		2	0	2	8		
		2	1			3	7

FORWARD COUNTING (6-69)

T	O	T	O	T	O	T	O
3	8	4	6	5	4	6	2
3	9						
4	0						
		4	9				
		5	0				
		5	1	5	9		
4	5	5	3	6	1	6	9

Date - ___________

Teacher's Signature - ___________

WHAT COMES AFTER (50-69)

T	O	T	O	T	O	T	O
5	6			5	4		
5	0			6	0		
6	2			6	7		
6	6			5	4		
6	8			5	1		
5	0			5	9		
5	5			5	3		
6	5			6	1		

Date - ____________

Teacher's Signature - ____________

WHAT COMES AFTER (1-69)

T	O	T	O	T	O	T	O
3	8			2	4		
5	7			6	0		
4	9			5	3		
6	4			1	1		
3	0			4	6		
3	4			3	0		
6	1				9		
1	5			6	6		

Date - ___________

Teacher's Signature - ___________

WHAT COMES IN BETWEEN (1-69)

T	O	T	O	T	O
5	0			5	2
3	9			4	1
4	7			4	9
4	3			4	5
6	8			7	0
2	1			2	3
1	8			2	0

WHAT COMES AFTER (1-69)

T	O	T	O	T	O	T	O
3	8			2	4		
5	7			6	0		
4	9			5	3		
6	4			1	1		
3	0			4	6		
3	4			3	0		
6	1				9		
1	5			6	6		

Date - ___________ Teacher's Signature - ___________

WHAT COMES IN BETWEEN (1-69)

T	O	T	O	T	O
5	0			5	2
3	9			4	1
4	7			4	9
4	3			4	5
6	8			7	0
2	1			2	3
1	8			2	0

NUMBER NAME (1)

	1		ONE				1			ONE		

Date - ____________

Teacher's Signature - ____________

NUMBER NAME (2)

	2		TWO				2		TWO			

Date - ____________

Teacher's Signature - ____________

NUMBER NAME (3)

	3		THREE					3		THREE			

Date - __________

Teacher's Signature - __________

NUMBER NAME (4)

4	FOUR	4	FOUR

NUMBER NAME (5)

5	FIVE	5	FIVE

Date - ____________

Teacher's Signature - ____________

MATCH NUMBER AND WORDS

9	TWO
1	NINE
5	ONE
3	FIVE
2	THREE

Date - ____________

Teacher's Signature - ____________

GREATER THAN / LESS THAN (> , <) (1-39)

T	O		T	O
1	2	☐	2	9
3	8	☐	2	4
1	5	☐		7
1	0	☐	1	9
1	3	☐	3	1
1	4	☐		4
2	5	☐	3	9

Date - ____________

Teacher's Signature - ____________

BIGGEST NUMBER (41-69)

Circle the biggest number in each row and write the number in the blank box.

T	O	T	O	T	O	T	O
4	1	4	3	5	1		
6	2	5	3	5	4		
6	1	6	5	6	0		
5	2	4	8	6	9		
4	7	6	6	5	4		
5	9	6	9	4	9		
6	1	5	0	4	5		
5	5	6	6	4	5		

SMALLEST NUMBER (41-69)

Circle the smallest number in each row and write the number in the blank box.

T	O	T	O	T	O	T	O
4	2	5	5	6	1		
6	7	6	1	6	6		
5	2	6	0	4	4		
4	9	6	2	5	0		
5	8	4	4	6	8		
6	4	4	2	4	0		
5	8	6	5	4	5		
4	7	6	6	5	5		

Date - ___________

Teacher's Signature - ___________

FORWARD COUNTING (70-79)

	T	O		T	O		T	O		T	O	
	7	0										

Date - ____________

Teacher's Signature - ____________

FORWARD COUNTING (16-79)

T	O	T	O	T	O	T	O
1	6			3	2	4	0
		2	5				
		2	6			4	2
				3	5		
				3	6	4	4
2	1					4	5
		3	0				
2	3			3	9	4	7

Date - ___________

Teacher's Signature - ___________

FORWARD COUNTING (16-79)

	T	O		T	O		T	O		T	O	
	4	8								7	2	
	4	9					6	5				
				5	8							
	5	1					6	7				
				6	0							
				6	1		6	9				
	5	4										
				6	3					7	9	

WHAT COMES AFTER (60-79)

T	O	T	O	T	O	T	O
6	8			6	4		
7	0			7	3		
6	2			6	7		
7	6			7	4		
7	8			7	1		
6	0			6	9		
7	5			6	3		
6	5			6	1		

WHAT COMES IN BETWEEN (1-79)

T	O	T	O	T	O
6	9			7	1
4	0			4	2
2	5			2	7
5	2			5	4
3	1			3	3
4	8			5	0
7	5			7	7

WHAT COMES BEFORE (60-79)

	T	O		T	O		T	O		T	O	
				7	8					6	2	
				6	0					6	8	
				6	7					7	0	
				7	4					7	9	
				6	5					7	3	
				6	1					6	4	
				7	7					6	8	
				6	3					7	1	

BACKWARD COUNTING (79-48)

	T	O		T	O		T	O		T	O	
	7	9								5	5	
							6	2				
				6	9							
							6	0				
										5	1	
										5	0	
				6	5							
	7	2					5	6				

Date - ____________

Teacher's Signature - ____________

COUNTING FORWARD AND BACKWARD

T	O	T	O	T	O	T	O
7	0	6	7	5	5	4	9
7	1						
				5	7		
						4	6
		6	3				
				6	0		
						4	3
		6	0				

PRACTICE COUNTING

	T	O		T	O		T	O		T	O	
		1		1	1		2	1		3	1	

Date - ____________

Teacher's Signature - ____________

PRACTICE COUNTING

	T	O		T	O		T	O		T	O	
	4	1		5	1		6	1		7	1	

GREATER THAN / LESS THAN (< , >) (1-59)

T	O		T	O
4	3	□	2	3
5	4	□	4	5
	7	□	1	7
2	0	□	2	8
5	0	□	3	0
	9	□	3	9
4	9	□	3	2

MISSING NUMBERS

SOME OF THE COACHES HAVE MISSING NUMBERS. FILL IN THE EMPTY SPACES.

BIGGEST NUMBER (51-79)

Circle the biggest number in each row and write the number in the blank box.

T	O	T	O	T	O	T	O
4	1	5	3	5	1		
7	2	6	3	7	4		
6	6	6	5	7	0		
5	2	7	8	6	9		
7	7	7	6	5	4		
5	9	7	9	5	7		
6	1	7	0	7	3		
5	5	7	2	7	5		

Date - ___________

Teacher's Signature - ___________

SMALLEST NUMBER (51-79)

Circle the smallest number in each row and write the number in the blank box.

T	O	T	O	T	O	T	O
6	2	5	5	7	3		
7	7	6	1	5	6		
5	2	7	0	5	4		
7	9	7	2	7	0		
5	1	7	4	6	1		
6	4	5	2	7	4		
5	8	6	5	7	5		
7	4	5	6	6	0		

Date - ____________

Teacher's Signature - ____________

FORWARD COUNTING (80-89)

	T	O		T	O		T	O		T	O	
	8	0										

Date - ____________

Teacher's Signature - ____________

FORWARD COUNTING (26-89)

T	O	T	O	T	O	T	O
2	6			4	2	5	0
						5	1
		3	6				
		3	7				
				4	6		
3	1					5	5
				4	8		
3	2						
				4	9		

Date - ____________

Teacher's Signature - ____________

FORWARD COUNTING (26-89)

T	O	T	O	T	O	T	O
5	8					8	2
		6	7			8	3
				7	6		
				7	7		
		7	0				
		7	1				
6	4					8	8
		7	3				

Date - ____________

Teacher's Signature - ____________

WHAT COMES AFTER (70-89)

T	O	T	O	T	O	T	O
8	7			8	2		
7	0			7	3		
8	2			7	7		
7	6			8	4		
7	8			8	1		
8	0			8	3		
7	5			8	5		
7	1			8	0		

Date - ___________

Teacher's Signature - ___________

WHAT COMES BEFORE (70-89)

T	O	T	O	T	O	T	O
		7	8			8	2
		7	7			8	8
		8	7			8	0
		7	4			7	9
		7	5			7	3
		7	1			8	4
		7	7			8	8
		8	3			8	1

Date - ____________

Teacher's Signature - ____________

WHAT COMES IN BETWEEN (1-89)

T	O	T	O	T	O
7	0			7	2
8	7			8	9
6	4			6	6
4	8			5	0
2	1			2	3
7	9			8	1
5	3			5	5

Date - ____________

Teacher's Signature - ____________

BACKWARD COUNTING
START FROM 89 AND GO TO 58

	T	O		T	O		T	O		T	O	
	8	9								6	5	
				8	0							
							7	1				
							7	0				
										6	1	
										6	0	
										5	9	
				7	4							

Date - ____________

Teacher's Signature - ____________

NUMBER NAMES

Trace on the dotted numbers and read aloud the number names.

GREATER THAN / LESS THAN (< , >) (1-89)

T	O		T	O
7	7	□	8	9
4	1	□	3	5
5	4	□	6	8
2	3	□	3	2
5	7	□	1	7
4	5	□	1	4
8	0	□	7	2

Date - ____________

Teacher's Signature - ____________

NUMBER NAME (6)

6	SIX	6	SIX

Date - ____________

Teacher's Signature - ____________

NUMBER NAME (7)

7	SEVEN	7	SEVEN

Date - ____________

Teacher's Signature - ____________

NUMBER NAME (8)

8	EIGHT	8	EIGHT

NUMBER NAME (9)

	9		NINE				9		NINE			

NUMBER NAME (10)

1	0	TEN		1	0	TEN

Date - ____________

Teacher's Signature - ____________

FORWARD COUNTING (90-100)

T	O		H	T	O		T	O		H	T	O
9	0						9	0				

Date - ___________

Teacher's Signature - ___________

REVISE COUNTING (1-100)
START FROM 1 AND GO UP TO 100

	T	O		T	O		T	O		T	O	
		1					3	1				
		2		1	7		3	2				
				1	8							
				1	9							
				2	0							
										5	1	
										5	2	
										5	3	
										5	4	
							4	0				
							4	1				
	1	2										
	1	3										
				2	9							
				3	0							

Date - ____________

Teacher's Signature - ____________

REVISE COUNTING (1-100)
START FROM 1 AND GO UP TO 100

		T	O		T	O		H	T	O		
		6	1		7	6						
					7	7						
					7	8						
									9	4		
									9	5		
									9	6		
		6	9									
		7	0					1	0	0		
					8	6						
					8	7						
		7	5									

Date - ____________

Teacher's Signature - ____________

ADDITION

$$\begin{array}{r} 1 \\ +\ 1 \\ \hline \\ \hline \end{array} \quad \begin{array}{r} 2 \\ +\ 1 \\ \hline \\ \hline \end{array} \quad \begin{array}{r} 3 \\ +\ 1 \\ \hline \\ \hline \end{array} \quad \begin{array}{r} 4 \\ +\ 1 \\ \hline \\ \hline \end{array}$$

$$\begin{array}{r} 5 \\ +\ 1 \\ \hline \\ \hline \end{array} \quad \begin{array}{r} 6 \\ +\ 1 \\ \hline \\ \hline \end{array} \quad \begin{array}{r} 7 \\ +\ 1 \\ \hline \\ \hline \end{array} \quad \begin{array}{r} 8 \\ +\ 1 \\ \hline \\ \hline \end{array}$$

$$\begin{array}{r} 7 \\ +\ 1 \\ \hline \\ \hline \end{array} \quad \begin{array}{r} 2 \\ +\ 1 \\ \hline \\ \hline \end{array} \quad \begin{array}{r} 3 \\ +\ 1 \\ \hline \\ \hline \end{array} \quad \begin{array}{r} 4 \\ +\ 1 \\ \hline \\ \hline \end{array}$$

Date - ____________

Teacher's Signature - ____________

ADDITION

5 + 3 = ___	2 + 3 = ___	7 + 2 = ___	4 + 4 = ___
3 + 4 = ___	6 + 2 = ___	5 + 2 = ___	8 + 4 = ___
7 + 2 = ___	3 + 3 = ___	3 + 5 = ___	4 + 5 = ___

Date - ________

Teacher's Signature - ________

SUBTRACTION

5	8	3	4
- 3	- 2	- 2	- 2
___	___	___	___

5	3	5	8
- 4	- 2	- 1	- 4
___	___	___	___

7	4	2	7
- 3	- 3	- 1	- 6
___	___	___	___

Date - ____________

Teacher's Signature - ____________

SUBTRACTION

5 - 2 ___	8 - 3 ___	7 - 6 ___	5 - 5 ___
6 - 3 ___	8 - 2 ___	8 - 1 ___	9 - 4 ___
9 - 3 ___	5 - 3 ___	4 - 1 ___	9 - 8 ___

Date - ____________

Teacher's Signature - ____________

BEFORE AND AFTER NUMBERS

BEFORE		AFTER
	79	
	64	
	83	
	92	
	90	
	55	
	11	
	26	

BEFORE		AFTER
	98	
	81	
	69	
	16	
	99	
	24	
	50	
	43	

Date - ____________

Teacher's Signature - ____________

ADD OR SUBTRACT AND MATCH

2 + 6	5
5 – 3	4
4 + 1	9
5 + 4	8
9 – 2	2
8 – 4	7

Date - ____________

Teacher's Signature - ____________

NUMBER NAMES

Circle the correct numbers for the given number names.

FIVE	6	5	2
THREE	4	1	3
TEN	10	2	5
ONE	9	3	1
EIGHT	8	2	6
FOUR	2	1	4
NINE	10	9	6
TWO	2	3	8

Date - ____________

Teacher's Signature - ____________

MISSING NUMBER

Fill in the missing numbers in each row.

35			38	39	
	82			85	86
		91	92		
70	71				
	49				53

NUMBERS FOR NUMBER NAMES

Number name	Number	Number name	Number
T E N		F I V E	
T W O		T H R E E	
S I X		N I N E	
O N E		E I G H T	
F O U R		S E V E N	

Date - ____________

Teacher's Signature - ____________

COUNT, MATCH AND WRITE

Count each group of objects. Draw a line from the number to the objects. Then, write the number name.

6

9

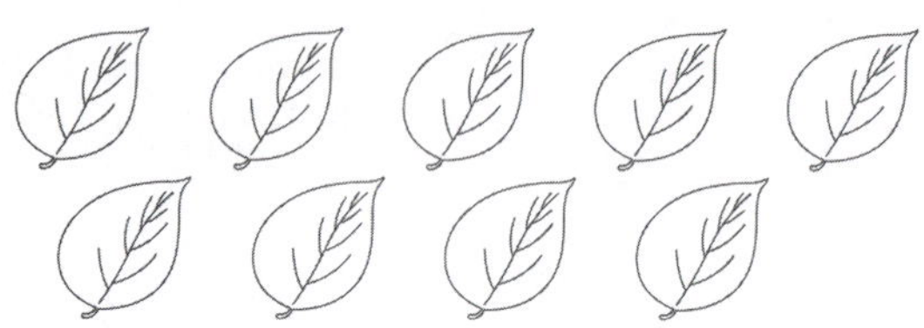

8

4

5

CONNECT THE NUMBERS

Connect the numbers in number order.

1	5	3	2	8	1
4	2	7	4	6	7
10	8	9	5	4	8
15	13	7	11	10	9
14	12	14	15	12	6
13	15	11	13	16	8
1	20	19	18	17	7

ADD AND SUBTRACT

Add to find the sum and subtract to find the difference.

ADD		SUBTRACT	
$\begin{array}{r} 2 \\ +\ 2 \\ \hline \end{array}$	$\begin{array}{r} 1 \\ +\ 2 \\ \hline \end{array}$	$\begin{array}{r} 4 \\ -\ 2 \\ \hline \end{array}$	$\begin{array}{r} 4 \\ -\ 4 \\ \hline \end{array}$
$\begin{array}{r} 3 \\ +\ 2 \\ \hline \end{array}$	$\begin{array}{r} 4 \\ +\ 5 \\ \hline \end{array}$	$\begin{array}{r} 5 \\ -\ 1 \\ \hline \end{array}$	$\begin{array}{r} 6 \\ -\ 3 \\ \hline \end{array}$
$\begin{array}{r} 7 \\ +\ 1 \\ \hline \end{array}$	$\begin{array}{r} 3 \\ +\ 6 \\ \hline \end{array}$	$\begin{array}{r} 8 \\ -\ 2 \\ \hline \end{array}$	$\begin{array}{r} 7 \\ -\ 1 \\ \hline \end{array}$

Prints Publications Pvt Ltd

PRINTS PUBLICATIONS PVT LTD

Kindergarten Series

PRE-KINDERGARTEN

(Series of 5 Books)

S. No.	ISBN	Titles
1	9789393674753	PATTERN WRITING
2	9789393674746	ENGLISH
3	9789393674739	MATHS
4	9789393674722	ENVIRONMENTAL STUDIES
5	9789393674784	ART & CRAFT

KINDERGARTEN-1

(Series of 7 Books)

S. No.	ISBN	Titles
1	9789393674890	PATTERN WRITING
2	9789393674814	ENGLISH
3	9789393674821	ENGLISH : Practice Book
4	9789393674845	MATHS
5	9789393674883	MATHS : Practice Book
6	9789393674838	ENVIRONMENTAL STUDIES
7	9789393674937	ART & CRAFT

KINDERGARTEN-2

(Series of 9 Books)

S. No.	ISBN	Titles
1	9789393674401	ENGLISH : Work Book
2	9789393674487	ENGLISH : Practice Book
3	9789393674548	ENGLISH : Assignment
4	9789393674944	MATHS : Work Book
5	9789393674951	MATHS : Assignment
6	9789393674968	MATHS : Practice Book
7	9789393674616	ENVIRONMENTAL STUDIES : Assignment
8	9789393674692	ENVIRONMENTAL STUDIES : Workbook
9	9789393674920	ART & CRAFT